CUCKOO

JOE SPARROW

'CUCKOO' BY JOE SPARROW
EDITED AND PUBLISHED BY ZAINAB AKHTAR

© SHORTBOX 2023

ISBN: 9781916096073
PRINTED IN THE UK

WWW.SHORTBOX.CO.UK

WITH THANKS TO BLANCA, ZAINAB, PETER, MARTIN AND LUKE,
AS WELL AS ANYONE WHO SAID ANYTHING ENCOURAGING.

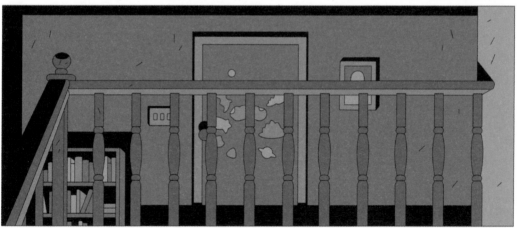

ALWAYS
SO ~~~~ !

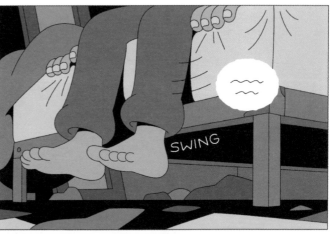

SWING

YOU
CAN'T JUST
~~~~

~~~~ MY
FEELINGS

~~~~
DIFFICULT
ENOUGH
WHEN

BECAUSE
WE CAN'T
AFFORD IT!

WELL, WHAT
DO YOU EXPECT
ME TO DO
ABOUT IT?!

I'M ALREADY
PAYING
HALF THE

UGH!

I SWEAR,
YOU NEVER
USED TO BE
LIKE THIS!

IT'S LIKE
YOU'RE A
WHOLE
DIFFERENT
PERSON
SOMETIMES!

SSSSHHPP

WHUDD

SHNK

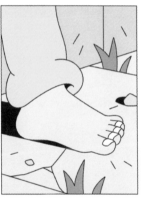

BLINK

WUMMMM

TOUCH

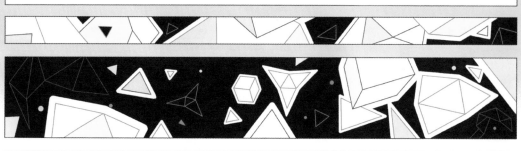

DOROTHY?

DOROTHY!

DOROTHY, HONEY

ARE YOU OKAY?

MBRBL.

MRB. WHAT?

WHERE 'M I?

YOU'RE IN THE **GARDEN**, SWEETIE.

FIVE

YEARS

LATER

RUB RUB

LAST NIGHT I DREAMT...

SOMETHING.

I'VE BEEN DREAMING A **LOT**, LATELY.

I THINK IT'S THE **HEAT**?

G'MORN'

UNSEASONABLY **WARM** NOVEMBER.

LAST NIGHT FELT...

DIFFERENT, THOUGH.

MORNING, SUNSHINE.

IT'S SO *WEIRD.*

THE STUFF THAT BUBBLES UP IN *DREAMS.*

MEMORIES....

OR JUST... *DREAMS OF MEMORIES,* I GUESS.

IT'S HARD TO TELL.

I HADN'T THOUGHT ABOUT THAT NIGHT IN *YEARS.*

THE TIME THEY FOUND ME IN THE *GARDEN.*

DID THAT EVEN *HAPPEN?*

MUM & DAD USED TO FIGHT A LOT MORE, BACK THEN.

THEY'RE WAY BETTER SINCE THE *SEPARATION.*

THINK THEY'RE FINALLY DIVORCING THIS YEAR.

THERE'S NO BAD FEELINGS ON *MY* END.

NO "WE BOTH LOVE YOU VERY MUCH" SIT-DOWN TALKS.

WE ALL GET WHAT'S *HAPPENING* HERE.

I TURNED **NINETEEN** A COUPLE OF MONTHS AGO.

BASICALLY AN ADULT.

MUCH ON AT UNI TODAY?

...AN **ADULT** WHO STILL LIVES WITH HER **MUM.**

UH

LIFE DRAWING.

& JUST WORKING ON OUR END-OF-YEAR PROJECT.

OH?

THAT SOUNDS **FUN.**

WORKING HARD?

...

27

DOROTHY?

BLIP

OH

LOTS OF, UH, IDEAS.

...

...

THAT'S GOOD.

IT'S A GOOD THING, YOU KNOW.

TO BE ABLE TO DO WHAT YOU LOVE.

I KNOW... IT'S NOT EASY, SOMETIMES.

BUT...

≶SIGH≶

I KNOW YOU'RE TRYING YOUR BEST.

SOMETIMES I FEEL LIKE I AM.

BUT I'M PROBABLY **NOT.**

MUM'S BEING NICE CALLING IT **"UNI"**, INCIDENTALLY.

IT'S A SMALL LOCAL COLLEGE.

WE COMPROMISED ON AN **ILLUSTRATION** COURSE.

ROOM 122

LESS FLOATY THAN **FINE ART.** MIGHT BE ABLE TO GET AN ACTUAL **JOB** AT THE END OF IT.

I THOUGHT ABOUT MOVING OUT, OBVIOUSLY.

THAT'S WHAT PEOPLE **NORMALLY** DO, RIGHT?

BUT I FIGURE I CAN SAVE UP MONEY LIVING AT HOME.

NO STUDENT LOANS.

NO BAGGAGE.

IT'S PARTLY ABOUT **MUM**, TOO.

SINCE **DAD** MOVED OUT.

IT'S NOT THAT I DON'T THINK SHE'D BE FINE ON HER OWN

IT'S JUST—

I GUESS I WORRY FOR HER.

SHE WORKS SO **HARD**.

NOT LIKE ME.

CAN'T EVEN START A FUCKING **ART PROJECT**.

THERE'S A HOSPITAL DOWN THE ROAD.

WE HEAR A LOT OF **SIRENS**.

ALL DAY. I STRUGGLE TO IMAGINE THE SCALE OF IT. **BIRTHS. INJURIES. DEATHS.** A MILLION "WORST-DAY-OF-MY-LIFES" PER HOUR.

BLENDING TO-GETHER INTO A SOLID, CONTINU-OUS **DRONE**.

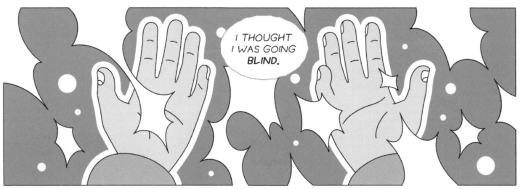

33

MY GP SAYS IT'S A **STRESS** THING.

"OCULAR MIGRAINES."

SHE GAVE ME A LEAFLET ABOUT **ANXIETY**.

I READ IT ON THE BUS HOME.

IT TALKED ABOUT SOME **BREATHING** EXERCISES...

... & STUFF LIKE "NO SCREENS BEFORE BED."

THAT ONE'LL BE **TOUGH**.

I PLAY VIDEOGAMES A LOT.

EVER SINCE I WAS **LITTLE**.

TOO MUCH, PROBABLY.

IT'S... SOMETHING I HAVE **CONTROL** OVER, I GUESS. IT'S **SATISFYING**.

TAKKA

B

SOMETIMES **ART** CAN BE SATISFYING, TOO.

– OR IT **USED** TO?

BACK WHEN I WAS A **KID**, AT LEAST.

I USED TO JUST DRAW... WHATEVER.

SKRTCH

WHATEVER CAME INTO MY HEAD.

BUT THE LINES WON'T DO WHAT I **WANT** ANYMORE.

THEY'RE CLUMSY. **DISTORTED.**

SKRR

FUCK.

FUZZY WITH ABORTED AFTERIMAGES.

RUB RUB

IT NEVER LOOKS HOW I **WANT.**

KLK

FUCK!!

COME ON, DOROTHY.

YOU CAN DOODLE IN YOUR SKETCHOOK **LATER.**

FWOP

FINISH UP THE DRAWING **FIRST,** PLEASE.

TEN MINUTES, EVERYONE!

ALRIGHT!

GOOD WORK, EVERYONE!

HAVE A NICE WEEKEND AND DON'T FORGET YOUR PROJECT REVIEWS NEXT WEEK!

TOC TOC TOC

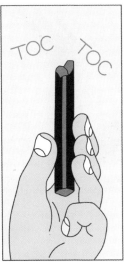

TOC TOC

MAYBE... ...I'M NOT CUT **OUT** FOR THIS.

SOMETIMES I THINK I'M NOT CUT OUT FOR **ANYTHING.**

MY GP HAD A NAME FOR **THIS**, TOO.

"CATASTROPHISING."

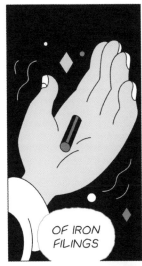

KLAT

NECEDE MALIS

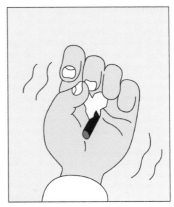

SOMETHING **EXTREMELY** FUCKED UP HAS HAPPENED TO ME IN THE LAST MONTH.

AFTER THE THING WITH THE **CHARCOAL**, I WAS CONVINCED I'D GONE NUTS.

LIKE, FULL BLOWN, KOO-KOO **CRAZY.**

THAT I'D BLACKED OUT, ARRANGED IT ALL ON THE FLOOR MYSELF?

OR **SOME-**THING.

BUT I HADN'T LOST ANY **TIME** THAT I COULD TELL.

5:47

IT GENUINELY HAPPENED IN THE BLINK OF AN EYE.

MY NEXT THOUGHT, EMBARRASS-INGLY, WAS "GHOSTS".

I GOOGLED THE HISTORY OF THE BUILDING.

NO **GRAVEYARDS** OR **MASS-MURDERERS** OF NOTE.

ALTHOUGH I GUESS BAD STUFF HAS HAPPENED **EVERYWHERE** IF YOU GO BACK FAR ENOUGH.

SO I TRIED TO JUST... **FORGET** ABOUT IT.

DISMISS IT AS A MIS-REMEMBERED **DAYDREAM.**

...WITH ABOUT AS MUCH SUCCESS AS YOU'D EXPECT.

IT KEPT **HAPPENING,** TOO.

NEVER IN THE **EXACT** SAME WAY.

STUFF JUST KINDA... **MOVING.** REARRANGING. WITHOUT ME **TOUCHING** IT.

AT FIRST IT SEEMED TO LINE UP WITH THE TIMES I WAS PARTICULARLY STRESSED?

WHICH, ADMITTEDLY, WAS **MOST** OF THE TIME AT THAT POINT.

EVENTUALLY MY MORE **METICULOUS** IMPULSES TOOK OVER.

I TRIED TO SEE IF THE EFFECT COULD BE REPLICATED **INTENTIONALLY.**

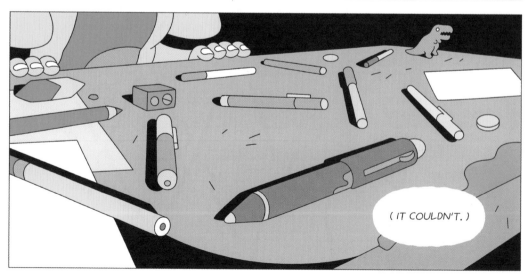

(IT COULDN'T.)

AT LEAST, NOT UNTIL I ELIMINATED A FEW VARIABLES.

FINALLY I STARTED TO ISOLATE THE FEELING I GET WHEN IT **DOES** HAPPEN.

LIKE PICKING OUT THE **MELODY** FROM A **BUSY SONG.**

FWISH

F**UCK**ING HELL!!

MATERIAL DOESN'T SEEM TO MATTER

AT FIRST I THOUGHT IT MIGHT BE **ELECTRICITY** OR **MAGNETS**...

BUT I DON'T THINK IT IS.

STUFF JUST... **MOVES.**

IT'S NOT QUITE LIKE I **MOVE** IT.

MORE LIKE I JUST MAKE IT REALLY **EASY** FOR IT TO GO A CERTAIN WAY, AND THEN IT **DOES.**

I CAN ONLY DO **LIGHT** STUFF SO FAR.

AND MORE THAN ONE THING AT A TIME IS **HARD.**

IT ALWAYS HAS THIS WEIRD **GEOMETRIC** FEEL TO IT, TOO.

KRUNK

WORKS BEST IN **STRAIGHT LINES** AND **SHARP ANGLES.**

CRUSSHH

LIKE THE OBJECT GETS **SNAPPED** TO AN UNDERLYING PATTERN

OR SOMETHING.

...

I DECIDED **NOT** TO TELL MY PARENTS.

THEY'VE GOT **ENOUGH** GOING ON RIGHT NOW.

I MEAN, WHAT COULD THEY DO IF THEY **KNEW**, EVEN?

"SORRY, YOUR DAUGHTER'S EITHER **MENTAL**..."

"...OR SHE CAN – **BEST CASE** – OCCASIONALLY MOVE PENCILS WITH HER MIND."

THERE'S NOBODY ELSE I CAN TELL ABOUT IT, REALLY.

GP OR POLICE SEEMS LIKE A BAD IDEA IF I DON'T WANT TO GET **SECTIONED**.

I'M NOT THAT CLOSE WITH PEOPLE FROM COLLEGE.

I HAD A FEW FRIENDS AT 6TH FORM BUT THEY ALL MOVED AWAY.

I'M HAPPY TO JUST KEEP IT TO MYSELF, FOR NOW AT LEAST.

KICK THAT DECISION DOWN THE **ROAD** A BIT.

IT'S ACTUALLY SORT OF **FUN**.

HAVING A LITTLE **SECRET**.

HAVING SOMETHING ONLY I CAN DO.

DONC

THERE AREN'T TOO MANY PLACES I CAN DO IT IN **PRIVATE**, THOUGH.

NOT IF I WANT TO TRY AND GET **BETTER** AT IT, ANYWAY.

TAK

I NEED **SPACE** TO REALLY **LET LOOSE**.

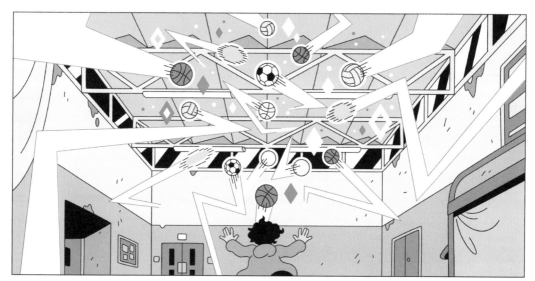

HELLO,
CHILD.

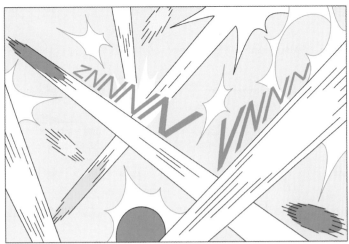

I REMEMBER IT NOW.

THAT **THING** IN THE GARDEN WHEN I WAS A KID.

IT'S LIKE MY **BRAIN** BLOCKED IT OUT.

WHAT THE **FUCK** WAS THAT?? JESUS FUCKING **CHRIST**.

LIKE A BIG... **SPIDER** MADE OF **GEOMETRY** OR SOMETHING?

KEEPS POPPING INTO MY **HEAD**. LIKE AN ANNOYING **TUNE**.

GOD WAS IT EVEN **REAL**?

A HALLUCI-NATION?

AM I EVEN THAT **IMAGINATIVE**??

I... DON'T THINK SO?

LIKE... **THAT'S** REAL, RIGHT?

THE **MESS** IN THE GYM?

FUCK. I'M TRYING TO THINK, DID I LEAVE **FINGERPRINTS** ON ANYTHING?

...SMALL BENEFIT OF **TELEKINESIS**, I GUESS.

STUPID.

I'LL JUST KEEP MY **HEAD DOWN.**

IT'LL BLOW OVER.

I'M FINE.

PFOO

IT'LL BE **FINE.**

ARE YOU **SURE** ABOUT THAT?

I –

WAIT, WHAT?

OH HEY, UH, LET ME—

WHAT IF I DO IT LIKE **THIS?**

IS THAT BETTER?

NOW WE CAN SEE WHO'S—

WHO?

WHO THE FUCK **ARE** YOU?

A—AND WHY ARE YOU **TALKING** IN MY HEAD?

HEY!

DIDN'T YOU EVER CONSIDER YOU MIGHT BE IN **MINE?**

YOU THINK SO LOUD I CAN HEAR YOU THROUGH THE **WALLS!**

WHAT?!

I'M JUST... **THANKING!**

I CAN'T THINK... **QUIETER!**

HEY, I'M NOT COM-PLAINING!

IT'S COOL.

NICE JOB WITH THE **GYM**, BY THE WAY!!

THAT **WAS** YOU, RIGHT?

IT SOUNDED **MAD!**

PLONK

· · ·

NOT FEELING CHATTY?

MAN, I GET IT.

· · ·

WHAT DO YOU **WANT.**

WHAT DO I WANT?

I WANT YOU TO DO IT.

DO THE **THING**.

I-I **DON'T** KNOW WHAT YOU'RE TALKING ABOUT.

COME ON!

YOU DON'T NEED TO BE **COY**.

I KNOW WHAT YOUR **DEAL** IS.

PSYCHIC POWERS.

TELEKINESIS. TELEPATHY. E-S-P.

WHATEVER THE FUCK.

HOW.

HOW DO YOU **KNOW** ABOUT THAT.

'COS I HAVE THEM **TOO**, OBVIOUSLY.

YOU COULD **TELL**, RIGHT?

WHEN I TOUCHED YOUR **ARM?**

YOU SEE THEM TOO, I BET.

THE SHAPES.

WHENEVER IT HAPPENS.

I THINK WE'RE THE SAME.

...OR AT LEAST... SIMILAR.

...

LOOK...

I—I'M SORRY FOR TAKING THE PISS, BEFORE.

IT'S JUST... HOW I DEAL WITH STUFF, Y'KNOW?

BUT IF WE CAN BOTH DO THIS STUFF...

...MAYBE WE CAN HELP EACH OTHER?

BUT FIRST

INDULGE ME.

I REALLY WANNA SEE YOU DO THE THING.

WITH MY OWN TWO LITTLE OLD EYES.

PLEEASE?

!!

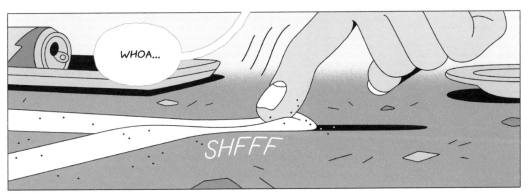

WHOA...

SHFFF

COOL, RIGHT?

CAN YOU...

CAN YOU SHOW ME HOW TO **DO** THAT?

O-ON **PURPOSE,** I MEAN

YEAH!

I MEAN, **PROBABLY,** RIGHT?

OH YEAH, SHIT.

MY NAME'S *ELLIE*, BY THE WAY.

NICE TO... *MEET YOU*, I GUESS.

...

OW!

D–DOROTHY.

I'M *DOROTHY*.

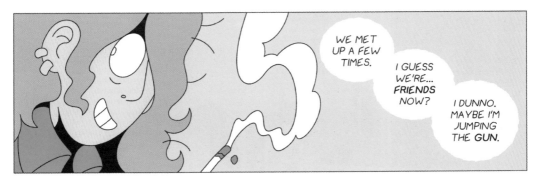

WE COMPARED EXPERIENCES, OBVIOUSLY.

WE THINK IT ALL HAPPENED ON THE **SAME NIGHT**.

FIVE YEARS AGO.

HERS LANDED IN A **PARK**.

SHE WOKE UP A FEW HOURS LATER, BY HERSELF.

SAME METEOR.

SAME WEIRD **CRYSTAL** THING.

SAME FLASH OF **LIGHT**.

SAME **SHAPES**.

SAME **POWERS**.

ALTHOUGH HERS STARTED SHOWING UP **LAST YEAR**.

83

WE ARRANGED TO MEET UP AT THE WEEKEND.

WE NEED A SAFE PLACE TO GO, THOUGH.

NOW THAT THE *GYM'S* OFF THE TABLE.

ELLIE SUGGESTED THIS *BIG PARK* NEARBY THAT SHE LIKES.

ONE OF THOSE HUGE LONDON ONES WITH LOTS OF DENSE TREES.

I WAS SCEPTICAL, BUT SHE RECKONS IT'S SAFE.

JUST THROUGH HERE.

ARE YOU SURE WE'RE ALLOWED THROUGH THERE?

WHAT?

I DOUBT IT, WHY WOULD THE FENCE BE THERE OTHER-WISE?

JESUS, THESE *BARS...*

D-DID YOU–

DID *I* BEND THEM?

NAH. IT WAS LIKE THAT WHEN I FOUND IT.

PROBABLY A CAR?

I THINK IF IT WAS *US* IT'D BE ALL *WEIRD* AND *GEOMETRIC*, OR SOMETHING.

SHIT, YOU'RE RIGHT.

SHFF

WHY D'YOU RECKON IT **DOES** THAT?

DUDE, I HAVE **NO** IDEA.

LOOKS COOL THOUGH, RIGHT?

...ANYWAY, WE'RE HERE!

WELCOME TO MY **HUMBLE ABODE!!**

SAFE FROM THE **PRYING EYES** OF THE WORLD.

...RELATIVELY SPEAKING.

WHOA.

SO MUCH **JUNK.**

ELLIE THERE ARE **CIDER BOTTLES.**

I THINK **TRAMPS** HANG OUT HERE.

YEAH, SOMETIMES, I THINK.

HAVEN'T SEEN ANY IN A **WHILE,** THOUGH.

TOSS

CATCH!!

WOAH—WUH!!!

I MEANT WITH YOUR **POWERS,** DUMMY!

OH.

Y-YEAH.

IS THIS A **RADIO?**

YUP!

FOUND IT IN SOME **CHARITY SHOP.**

CHECK **THIS** OUT!

HELLO DOROTHY DO YOU READ ME DOROTHY!

!

K SHHKLO DOROTHY DO YOU READ ME DOROTHY

COOL, ISN'T IT?

HOW'D YOU THINK IT WORKS?

I DUNNO.

JUST SORT OF **THINK** IN ITS DIRECTION.

RADIO WAVES OR SOMETHING.

IT'S PRETTY EASY!

TRY IT.

HELLO MY NAME IS DOROTHY HELLO HELLO

HELLO MY NAME IS DOROTHY HELLO HELLO

IT'S **NICE**, THERE.

SOMETHING WEIRDLY **CALMING** ABOUT BEING SURROUNDED BY **TREES.**

WEEKEND MEETUPS BECAME A REGULAR THING PRETTY QUICKLY.

HEY, WHAZZIS?

SKETCH-BOOK?

OH. Y-YEAH.

I JUST SORT OF... DOODLE IN THERE.

WHEN I'M STRESSED.

ALIENS.

IT'S **CLEARLY** ALIENS, RIGHT?!

REALLY? YOU DON'T THINK IT WAS JUST LIKE A...

RADIOACTIVE... ROCK?

NAH

RADIATION GIVES YOU **CANCER**

NOT SUPER-POWERS.

WE BOTH **SAW** THAT THING.

IT CAME FROM **SPACE**

IT WAS **ALIVE**

ALIENS!

· · ·

OKAY

WHY **POWERS,** THEN?

MAYBE IT'S A **PRESENT** FOR HUMANITY?

A LITLE **GIFT!**

"HERE YOU GO, LITLE MONKEYS!

NOW, **FLY!**"

95

HEH.

MAYBE.

OR IT **COULD** BE...

AN **ALIEN INVASION!!**

HMM.

PRETTY **SHITE** INVASION, THOUGH?

IF THEIR **BIG** TACTIC IS TO GIVE THE INVADEES **SUPER-POWERS** & THEN **VANISH**?

HAHA. YEAH

MY POINT IS, IF IT **IS** PART OF SOME **BIG** PLAN...

...IT'S CLEARLY **NOT** ONE WE'RE **IN** ON.

MAYBE WE'RE **NOT MEANT** TO KNOW.

MAYBE IT'S LIKE A **TEST**

JUST TO SEE WHAT WE **DO** WITH IT.

YEAH.

OR, LIKE...

LIKE A **PUZZLE** FOR US TO FIGURE OUT.

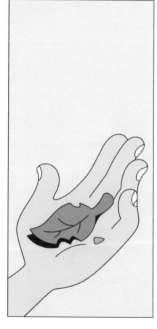

I'M HERE AND AT **MUM'S** ABOUT 50/50 OVER THE CHRISTMAS HOLIDAY.

ELLIE'S UP NORTH AT HER PARENTS.

SO OUR PARK SESSIONS ARE ON HOLD.

I LIKE MY DAD.

I THINK I GET MY MORE **CREATIVE** IMPULSES OFF HIM.

FRACTALS

GCSE MATHS

HE'S A **MATHS** TEACHER.

I USED TO LOVE LISTENING TO HIM TELL ME ABOUT ESOTERIC **MATHY** STUFF WHEN I WAS A KID.

IMAGINARY NUMBERS AND UNCOUNTABLE INFINITIES AND PARADOXES.

HE'D ALWAYS LOSE ME WITH THE **EXPLANATIONS**

(I WAS NEVER A **SUPER BRIGHT** KID.)

BUT THERE WAS SOMETHING ALMOST **MYSTICAL** ABOUT IT ALL.

LIKE ARCANE **LORE.**

MUM'S MORE RELIABLE, MORE **GROUNDED.**

MORE... **MORAL,** SOMEHOW.

HER ONLY INTEREST IN NUMBERS IS WHAT THEY REPRESENT IN THE **REAL WORLD.**

PAYCHECKS. SPREADSHEETS.

HER HOUSE IS A DOCUMENT TO MY GROWTH.

A GALLERY OF FAIRGROUND MIRRORS

IN SOME ERAS I'M **UNRECOGNISABLE.**

MUM USED TO JOKE THAT THE **FAIRIES** MUST HAVE SWAPPED ME OUT FOR ANOTHER KID.

STILL, WE'VE ALWAYS BEEN CLOSE.

I SPENT CHRISTMAS EVE AT HERS.

WE DID PRESENTS, BUT LIKE

LITTLE ONES.

– OF ENGLAND NOW FORECASTING A FURTHER YEAR OF RECESESSION –

SHE'S STILL ON JOBSEEKERS.

I DON'T THINK WE CAN AFFORD OUR MORTGAGE, EVEN WITH DAD'S HELP.

WE MIGHT BE MOVING IN THE NEW YEAR.

I CAN'T READ HER MIND.

(IT DOESN'T WORK THAT WAY, UNFORTUNATELY).

EVEN SO, I CAN TELL SHE WORRIES A LOT.

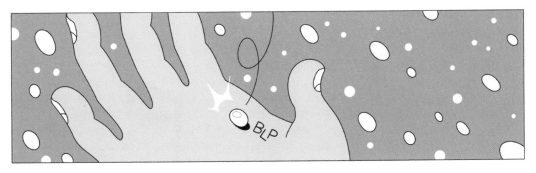

ELLIE CAME HOME IN A PRETTY BAD MOOD.

(THE FIRST I'VE SEEN HER IN, I THINK)

SHE DOESN'T GET ON WITH HER FAMILY.

THEY'RE, LIKE, MEGA-TORIES OR SOMETHING.

SHE TALKED MY EAR OFF ABOUT IT FOR A WHILE.

IT WAS CLEAR SHE NEEDED TO VENT.

SO I JUST LISTENED.

I TAUGHT HER SOME OF MY BREATHING TECHNIQUES, TOO.

SNIFF

SNIFFF

SHE BOUNCED BACK PRETTY QUICK.

OUR POWERS AREN'T SO MUCH GETTING **STRONGER** AS...

I'M NOT SURE HOW TO **PUT** IT.

MORE FINELY **DETAILED?**

LIKE THE RESOLUTION GOING UP ON A VIDEO.

NOT JUST **MOVING** THINGS.

CHANGING THEM, TOO.

THUNK

COLLEGE IS **DULL** BY COMPARISON.

I MEAN, WHY WOULDN'T IT BE?

EDUCATION IS FOR PEOPLE WHO DON'T KNOW WHAT THEY ARE.

I KNOW WHAT I AM.

I'M ME.

I'M THIS.

AFTER A WHILE I STARTED SKIPPING LECTURES ENTIRELY.

I MEAN, IT'S AN ART COURSE, SO THERE AREN'T MANY.

WE DON'T JUST STICK TO THE PARK. SOMETIMES WE HEAD INTO TOWN, TOO.

IT'S A BIG CITY, AFTER ALL.

TONS OF STUFF JUST A TUBE OR A BUS RIDE AWAY.

NOW SHOWING: JOHN CARPENTER'S T

STUFF I'D **NEVER** HAVE DONE ON MY OWN.

SCREE

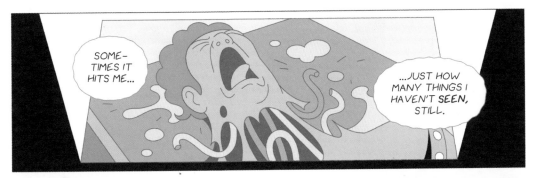

SOME-TIMES IT HITS ME...

...JUST HOW MANY THINGS I HAVEN'T **SEEN**, STILL.

HOW MANY THINGS I HAVEN'T **DONE**.

OR **FELT**.

I'VE NEVER **SMOKED**.

SCREE

HEUUGHFÝ

NEVER GOTTEN PROPERLY **DRUNK**.

NEVER HAD AN ACTUAL *JOB.*

NEVER HAD A BOY-FRIEND.

OR A *GIRL-FRIEND,* OR *WHATEVER.*

I GUESS I'VE HAD A PRETTY *SHELTERED* EXISTENCE IN A LOT OF WAYS.

I DON'T KNOW WHY I WAS SO *BORING* BEFORE.

WHY I WASN'T DOING THIS STUFF *ALREADY.*

HOW THEY SEEM TO FIT SO **EASILY** INTO IT ALL.

THEY **BARELY** SEEM TO EVEN **TRY.**

THEY JUST SLOT RIGHT INTO PLACE.

EUGH.

SOME DAYS IT'S LIKE A **CONSTANT, CONSCIOUS** EFFORT NOT TO PANIC.

VVRRRRRRR

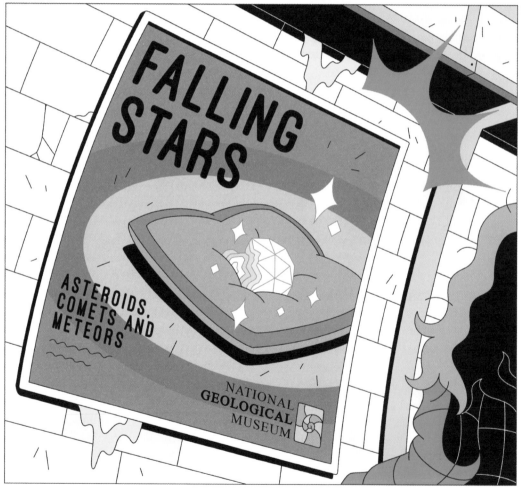

"ORIGINALLY THOUGHT TO BE A PART OF THE YEARLY **ORIONID** METEOR SHOWER, THIS SPECIMEN IS NOW THOUGHT TO BE MUCH OLDER AND FROM MUCH FURTHER AWAY.

"PERHAPS PRE-DATING THE EARTH AND SOME STARS IN OUR STELLAR NEIGHBOURHOOD."

"UNLIKE MOST STONY IRON METEORITES, IT IS COMPOSED OF A COMPLEX LATTICE OF MANY UNUSUAL ELEMENTS IN A CRYSTALLINE STRUCTURE.

"SCIENTISTS ARE CURRENTLY UNSURE EXACTLY HOW IT FORMED."

APPARENTLY IT'S BEEN TRAVELLING AT LEAST **FIVE BILLION** YEARS.

FUCKING **MENTAL**.

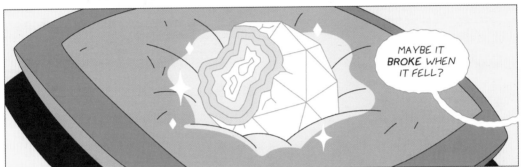

CAN YOU **HEAR** THAT?

WHAT?

I THINK ...

IT'S DOING THE SAME THING **WE DO.**

I THINK I CAN HEAR IT... **THINKING.**

DO YOU THINK IT'S...

TRYING TO **COMMUNICATE,** OR SOMETHING?

...

IT'S... HARD TO **MAKE** OUT.

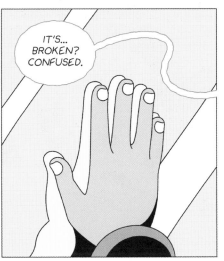

IT'S... BROKEN? CONFUSED.

I – I THINK

I THINK IT'S–

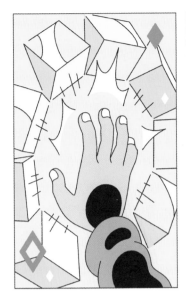

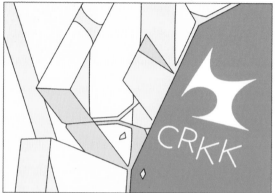

CRKK

HOOO

THANKS.

THAT **HELPED**.

FUCK.

WH—WHAT **TIME** IS IT?

PROBABLY NEED TO GET BACK.

I'UNNO.

MAYBE— WOAH.

LIKE **NINE**.

D—DON'T THEY LOCK UP THE PARK GATES AT NIGHT?

THE **MAIN** ENTRANCES, YEAH.

... I MEAN YOU COULD STICK AROUND FOR A BIT IF YOU WANTED?

NOT LIKE THOSE GATES ARE GONNA GET **MORE** LOCKED.

NICE LITTLE WALK AND TALK MIGHT HELP CALM YOU DOWN?

...

I HATE IT.

I WISH I WAS **DIFFERENT**.

I WISH I WAS A **WHOLE DIFFERENT PERSON**.

I THINK...

⟩PFOO⟨

THAT'D BE A **SHAME**.

I LIKE YOU HOW YOU ARE.

YOU'LL GET **BETTER**.

YOU JUST GOTTA LEARN TO SEE THE **GOOD** OUTCOMES AS WELL AS THE **BAD**.

YEAH.

IT'S JUST SO HARD NOT TO SEE EVERY POTENTIAL **DISASTER**.

WAITING OUT THERE IN THE **DARK**.

JUST OUT OF –

– SIGHT ⟩⟨

M—MY **PARENTS** BROUGHT ME HERE WHEN I WAS A KID.

THEY'RE LIKE, STATUES THAT **QUEEN VICTORIA** MADE, OR SOMETHING.

WHY DO THEY LOOK SO...

LIKE **THAT?**

OH I, UH, THINK THEY MADE THEM BEFORE THEY PROPERLY KNEW WHAT DINOSAURS **LOOKED** LIKE.

GOD.

I REMEMBER BEING **TERRIFIED** OF THEM.

LIKE, I WAS CONVINCED THEY WERE STILL **ALIVE.**

THUNGG

H—HEY! WHAT ARE YOU **DOING!?**

HOP

ELLIE!

ELLIE, COME **ON!**

PLACE

ELLIE THIS IS **DUMB** AND IT'S ONLY GONNA MAKE THINGS **WORSE**.

WHO CARES.

SEE IT AS A LITTLE EXERCISE.

FORGET ABOUT EVERYTHING ELSE.

I CAN'T FORGET EVERY-THING.

I KNOW. IT'S OKAY.

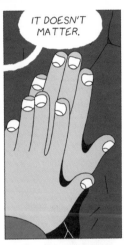

IT DOESN'T MATTER.

JUST **TRUST** ME.

...

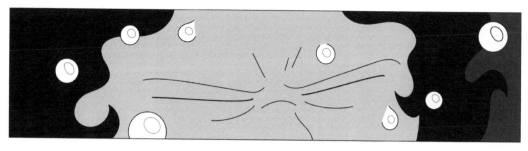

SEE? FEELS GOOD, RIGHT?

VWUMMM

141

WH–WHAT

TKK

KRK

HEY WHAT'S... WHAT'S WRONG?

WHAT THE FUCK IS...

WHAT IS

HEYA

HAVE YOU SEEN THE NEWS?!

A BOMB WENT OFF IN A MUSEUM, OR SOMETHING.

NOBODY SEEMS TO KNOW ANYTHING YET.

I GOT A PHONE CALL FROM THE **COLLEGE.**

THEY WANT YOU TO COME IN FOR A MEETING WITH THE **COURSE HEAD.**

THEY SAID THEY HAVEN'T SEEN YOU ON CAMPUS IN **TWO WEEKS.**

THEY WANT TO KNOW IF THEY CAN **DROP** YOU FROM THE COURSE.

WHICH –

Y'KNOW

DOROTHY I'M **FINE** WITH

I JUST... WANT TO **KNOW.**

RUB

LIKE I **THOUGHT** THIS WAS WHAT YOU **WANTED?**

THE **COURSE** AND ALL?

EXPLOSION AT NA

...

I DON'T **KNOW.**

I–I'M SORRY.

WELL IT'D BE **NICE** IF YOU COULD FIGURE THAT OUT.

BECAUSE, I MEAN, IT'S NOT **FREE,** IS IT?

DOROTHY.

SHUT

-SIGH-

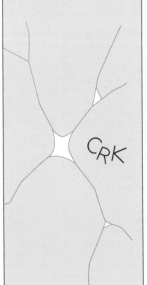

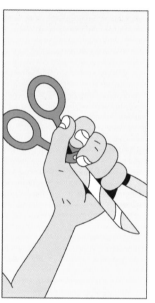
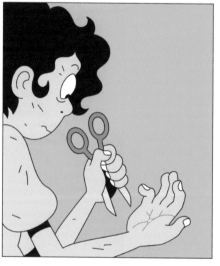

H–HEY ELLIE.

I... BETTER, I THINK.

HEY, CAN WE MEET UP TODAY?

JUST TO... TO **TALK?**

NO. NOT BACK IN THE PARK. NOT **YET.**

...IS THERE SOMEWHERE ELSE?

I MEAN YOU COULD COME TO **MINE,** IF YOU WANT. MY FLAT-MATE'S OUT AT WORK SO SHE WOUN'T BE AROUND.

YEAH YEAH, IT'LL BE FINE.

I'LL TEXT YOU THE ADDRESS.

DON'T WORRY.

IT'S **FINE.** IT'S GONNA BE **FINE.**

HEY!

YO.

YOU SLEEP MUCH?

...

A LITTLE.

OH **DOROTHY!**

HUG

155

...THAT ONE'S CALLED THE **MARSEILLES** TAROT.

I ALSO GOT A COOL BOOK ON THIS THING CALLED THE **AKASHIC RECORDS**.

YOU'RE WELCOME TO BORROW WHATEVER.

SORRY, HAHA.

I GUESS THIS STUFF ISN'T REALLY WHAT YOU WANTED TO TALK ABOUT.

DOES IT FEEL **WEIRD**?

YOUR **HAND**, I MEAN.

NAH. I LIKE LISTENING TO YOU TALK.

THE CRACK'S STILL THERE, BUT LIKE...

IT'S **HEALING**?

I MEAN...

THAT'S **GOOD**, RIGHT?

ADD **REGENERATION** TO YOUR GROWING LIST OF POWERS.

HEH. I GUESS.

BUT THIS IS...

THIS ISN'T **HUMAN**, IS IT?

MAYBE OUR BODIES CAN'T HANDLE IT?

MAYBE IT'S... **TRANSFORMING** US.

WHAT IF IT'S SOME KINDA **SPACE VIRUS**.

OR LIKE, TURNING US TO **STONE** OR SOMETHING?

HMMMMMM.

I THINK WE PROBABLY HAVE **TWO** OPTIONS.

ONE'S WEIRDER THAN THE OTHER.

NUMBER ONE, WE GO TO A HOSPITAL AND GET CHECKED OUT.

BUT LET'S BE REAL HERE, **NO** NHS DOCTOR IS GONNA KNOW WHAT'S GOING ON WITH US

OR BE ABLE TO HELP.

ALTHOUGH MAYBE WE'LL HELP ADVANCE **SCIENCE** OR SOMETHING.

AND NUMBER TWO?

WHAT'S NUMBER TWO?

I'M **GLAD** YOU ASKED

OKAY. SO **ASSUMING** I'M **RIGHT** AND IT'S **ALIENS**

AND **ASSUMING** THEY DID THIS TO US **KNOWINGLY**

WE JUST ASK **THEM**.

THE ALIENS.

...HOW?!

NO FUCKING CLUE.

HAHA

W-WHAT IF THIS IS **DANGEROUS?**

WHAT IF WE GET **ELECTROCUTED** OR SOMETHING??

WHAT IF... WHAT IF NOTHING TALKS **BACK?**

WHAT IF-

DOROTHY IT'S GONNA BE **FINE.**

WE'LL FIGURE IT OUT.

WE'RE IN THIS **TOGETHER.**

...

OKAY.

I DON'T... FEEL ANY-THING.

MAYBE... TRY TALKING LIKE **THIS?**

OH. YEAH.

JUST... REACH OUT, I GUESS.

SAME AS BEFORE.

TRY TO RELAX.

DEFOCUS.

WAIT, I CAN–

I THINK I CAN **HEAR** SOME-THING.

THERE'S–

167

174

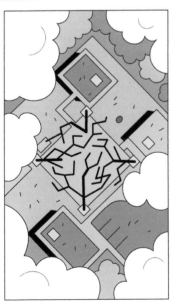

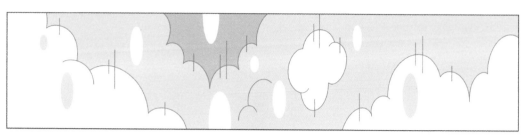

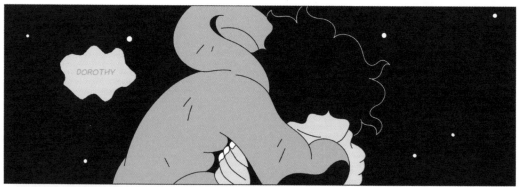

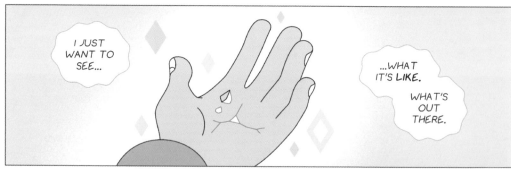

204

GOD.

DOESN'T IT LOOK **PRETTY**, THOUGH?

FROM **THIS** ANGLE, AT LEAST.

PUTS STUFF IN **PERSPEC-TIVE**.

206

HEY,
MUM.

I KNOW I'VE
BEEN A BIT
ALL OVER
THE PLACE
LATELY...

...
AND I'M
SORRY.

I KNOW IT'S... NOT BEEN **EASY** WITH ME, SOMETIMES.

I KNOW I'M NOT EXACTLY THE DAUGHTER I **SHOULD** BE.

MY LIFE ALWAYS FELT LIKE SUCH A **MESS.**

LIKE... **WHITE NOISE.** JUST **SOUND,** WITHOUT PURPOSE OR MEANING.

NOTHING MADE SENSE.

NOTHING FELT **RIGHT.**

THE MUSIC.

"CUCKOO"

TELEPATHY

HI.

PSYCHIC
HEADACHE

PHYSICAL
DISTORTIONS

HELLO.

TELE
KINESIS

DOROTHY (THEA)

:R?

ARTIST
?

CONNECTED
TO FEELINGS?

SLIGHTLY LESS
EARLY SKETCHES
(BUT STILL
PRETTY EARLY)